The Amazing Benefits of Meditation

Living the Life You've Always Wanted to Live

Blair Abee

Energetic Wave Publishing
Vallejo, California

Blair Abee/Energetic Wave Publishing
139 Dyer Ct.
Vallejo, California 94591
www.HiCMeditation.com

Book Layout ©2017 BookDesignTemplates.com. v1

Ordering Information:
Quantity sales. Special discounts are available on quantity purchases by corporations, associations, and others. For details, contact the "Special Sales Department" at the address above.

The Amazing Benefits of Meditation/ Blair Abee. —1st ed.
ISBN 978-1-7344754-3-2

Contents

The Benefits of Meditation 4

Traditional Meditation and Higher Consciousness Meditation (HCM)..7

Lessening Stress, Increasing a Sense of Well-Being 13

Physical, Mental, Emotional, Spiritual Health and Other Benefits 19

Creativity and Problem Solving 29

Why Does Meditation Work the Way it Does for Healing? 39

Amplifying the Natural Benefits of Meditation.........................43

Conclusion and Next Steps..47

About the Author, My Story..51

Energetic Wave Publishing Resources for You

These are worrisome and stressful times. Meditation and Higher Consciousness is your path to freedom and abundance. Blair offers a number of resources to you the reader to help you on your Journey to Illumination, Soul Contact, and freedom from the human condition.

His **complete book list** at Amazon includes:

- The Many Amazing Benefits of Meditation: Living the Life You've Always Wanted to Live
- The Meditation Book: The Essential Meditation for Beginners to Find Peace, Reduce Stress, and Improve Mental Health
- The Mindfulness Book: The Practical Meditation Book to Relieve Stress, Find Peace, and Cultivate Gratitude
- The Abundance Book: The Spiritual Path to Abundance (available September 2021)
- Homage to Spirit: Poems to Elevate Consciousness

In addition, he offers **a 6-hour class** on "Meditation and Abundance" every other month, covering:

- Sit-down meditation using his Higher Consciousness Meditation process
- Mindfulness meditation using his Higher Consciousness Mindfulness exercises
- Creating abundance from a spiritual perspective
- Health and wellness, with meditation and other techniques to create optimum health

Contact him for the next class at Blair@HigherConsciousnessMeditation.com.

For those interested in **one-on-one meditation and awareness consultation** Blair offers 1 hour coaching

sessions. Contact him at
Blair@HigherConsciousnessMeditation.com.

His **website** HiCMeditation.com is chock full of information about Higher Consciousness Meditation topics:

- A blog with in-depth articles about meditation topics and wellness issues
- Sample chapters of his books
- Spiritual poems
- A curated shopping area for products he recommends to help you create a healthy home environment with high vibrational qualities—things he and his wife have and love in their home
- A newsletter signup

Lastly, you can get a morning inspirational quote/picture in your Facebook, Instagram or Twitter feed by going to https://www.facebook.com/authormeditation, https://www.instagram.com/hicmeditation/ or https://twitter.com/AbeeBlair. 365 **Daily Vibes** will make you smile and lift up for a year.

CHAPTER 1.

The Benefits of Meditation

The benefits of meditation are many and far reaching. As each year goes by new scientific research emerges to reveal what mystics and meditators have known for many centuries—meditation is an elixir unlike any other to improve your physical, mental, emotional, and spiritual well-being.

This book will examine the many benefits from a scientific perspective as well as from a mystical perspective ("mystical" defined as direct contact with Spirit, God, Higher Consciousness, or whatever definition you want to use for the experience of the Eternal).

The book is the first in a series of books, called the Higher Consciousness Series, that I am writing to explore and expand on our notions of who we are, why we are here on Planet Earth, and where we might be going as individuals and as a species. The second book, which is also now available at Amazon Kindle and other publishing platforms, is called **The Meditation Book: The Essential Meditation for Beginners to Find Peace, Reduce Stress, and Improve Mental Health**, and is a deep dive into the practice of meditation and some of the methods I have developed to enhance traditional meditation practices.

I think you will find this second book a quick and exciting read, revealing to beginners, and stimulating for experienced spiritual explorers alike.

Benefits of Meditation

The benefits of meditation that practitioners have experienced and reported are nothing short of amazing. Meditation can help you:

- Reduce the feeling of being stressed out and overwhelmed by life
- Be more peaceful and loving
- Address certain health concerns
- Look better, feel better and be better
- Be more alive, joyful, and self-confident
- Deal more effectively with life's ups and downs, twists and turns
- Be more creative and make better decisions
- Be more awake and aware
- Attract good people, things, and circumstances

You may think that I'm exaggerating the benefits with this list, but I have personally experienced these improvements, as have many others, anecdotally, throughout human history. Significant scientific research has been done that confirms many of the anecdotal experiences that have been reported.

CHAPTER 2.

Traditional Meditation and Higher Consciousness Meditation (HCM)

Traditional Meditation

The *Miriam-Webster Dictionary* defines meditation as "the act or process of spending time in quiet thought. Continuous and profound contemplation or musing on a subject or series of subjects of a deep or abstruse nature; 'the habit of meditation is the basis for all real knowledge (unattributed).'"

Wikipedia does a better job in its definition of meditation:

> Meditation is a practice in which an individual trains the mind or induces a mode of consciousness, either to realize some benefit or as an end in itself. The term "meditation" (much like the term "sports") refers to a broad variety of practices that includes techniques designed to promote relaxation, build internal energy or life force (*qi*, *ki*, *prana*, etc.) and develop compassion, love, patience, generosity and forgiveness. A particularly

ambitious form of meditation aims at effortlessly sustained single-pointed concentration meant to enable its practitioner to enjoy an indestructible sense of well-being while engaging in any life activity.

The word *meditation* carries different meanings in different contexts. Meditation has been practiced since antiquity as a component of numerous religious traditions and beliefs. Meditation often involves an internal effort to self-regulate the mind in some way. Meditation is often used to clear the mind and ease many health issues, such as high blood pressure, depression, and anxiety. It may be done sitting, or while walking with awareness. For instance, Buddhist monks (and others, ed.) involve awareness (called 'mindfulness") in their day-to-day activities as a form of mind-training. Prayer beads or other ritual objects are commonly used during meditation in order to keep track of or remind the practitioner about some aspect of the training.

Among the ideas expressed in these definitions and in the Wikipedia commentary that I think are salient:

- Meditation has been used for centuries to quieten the mind until thoughts cease for short or extended periods of time, or to "induce a mode of consciousness" that, in spiritual traditions, brought the meditator closer to God or generated a heightened spiritual state.
- Meditation is not a religion, nor does it conflict with any religion. It has been typically employed by the mystical forms of our familiar spiritual traditions, the Kabbalist form of Judaism, Yoga in Hinduism, Sufism in Islam, and Christian Hesychasm.

However, another term for meditation is "silent prayer", a technique of approaching deity in a listening mode rather than an asking mode, a technique employed by almost all religions. Silent prayer is desiring to have an experience of deity, or a sense of the "presence" of Spirit, rather than asking deity to fulfill a wish.

- The story of Gautama Buddha and his awakening is one of the most well-known directly tied to meditation. Enlightenment through meditation came after he spent many years exploring numerous spiritual traditions and studying with many different teachers in India.
- In Buddhist meditation the spiritual goal is to reach a state of Nirvana, an elevated state of awareness which very few who attempt this approach manage to achieve. Those who do get there are thought of, and revered, as enlightened.
- Traditional meditation is difficult because it assumes that the mind is a wild horse that needs to be tamed and uses sitting quietly, observing one's thoughts, and being aware of one's breath as its process. Sometimes, meditation incorporates the repeating of mantras (sacred words) and/or the use of objects (beads, a rosary, etc.) to self-regulate and/or subdue the mind. Unfortunately, such an approach often takes years and years of practice to be successful; to tame that wild horse is not easy.
- I have been meditating for over 40 years, beginning at Swami Satchidananda's Integral Yoga Institute in San Francisco, and have explored a number of other traditions. I have found that the methods I tried were something of a quest--an engagement with my mind until it began to quieten down a little, and then more and

more. I experienced it as a wrestling match, and many others have said the same thing, to take that wild horse that is the mind and tame it. This is difficult and many people quit before ever getting there. It's hard. Worthwhile, for sure, but tough for most of us.

- Meditation has been used increasingly in the West for secular purposes, for the scientifically proven benefits it grants—including the easing of health issues, such "high blood pressure, depression, and anxiety" as mentioned above.
- Jon Kabat-Zinn, founder of the Mindfulness-Based Stress Reduction program in the late '70s, has shown scientifically that mindfulness increases the body's ability to heal and includes a shift from a tendency to use the right prefrontal cortex instead of the left prefrontal cortex. This shift is associated with a trend away from depression and anxiety and towards happiness, relaxation, and emotional balance.
- Mindfulness induces a state of "moment to moment non-judgmental awareness" using, among other things, thought and breath observation, body scanning, mindful walking and being aware of the taste and texture of the food that we eat, among other techniques. It's a way, with acute observation, to quieten the mind and allow Fifth Dimensional Consciousness to flow into 3rd dimensional situations.

Higher Consciousness Meditation (HCM)

As a result of a dramatic increase in the depth and breadth of my meditation practice caused by a series of personal traumas (see Appendix 1 for details), I took a very deep dive into my traditional meditation practice and developed my own system which I call Higher Consciousness Meditation (HCM).

HCM builds on traditional meditation and is, in my opinion, the next step in the evolution of meditation, as well as the next step in human evolution. HCM is built around a core process that is simple and straightforward, but very powerful (detailed in my second book, The Meditation Book. In addition, HCM offers a variety of triggers and tricks that add to the core process' effectiveness and offers a variety of them to keep the practice interesting (mentioned in Book 2 but detailed in The Mindfulness Book, (Higher Consciousness Series, Book 3). Some of you may find that the core process does not suit you and that mindfulness techniques, triggers and tricks are more to your liking.

Higher Consciousness

HCM is one method to acquaint you with your Soul, or Higher Consciousness, and to develop an awareness of this state for yourself. To become Awake and Aware (most of my midsentence capitalizations call attention to the spiritual nature of the word) is a radical shift, mind you, one in which you will see yourself, others and your world, from a quite different perspective.

Developing a relationship with our Soul, our Higher Consciousness, is an idea that has been taught by the world's Master Teachers for centuries—the idea of "Spirit Within" us. I found that all I had to do was turn Within, using HCM or mindfulness, and It, my Soul, would come flooding to meet me.

One answer, then, to the question, "Why meditate?" is that by using Higher Consciousness Meditation we can get in touch with this "one Spirit" and grow and evolve into a being of Higher Consciousness. Making it possible for us to live from a state of greater awareness, of Oneness. Then we can approach life as the Master Teachers did, with magnificence, as bearers of unconditional love and wisdom, illumined with the Light of the Spirit of The ALL, God, and worthy of receiving "all that will be added" to us. (The ALL is a term I first came across in the writings of Hermes Trigmustus, an ancient Egyptian philosopher).

The true Self, Higher Consciousness, has also been referred to as "Christ Consciousness", "Buddha Mind", "Enlightenment" and is within us all, waiting to be discovered. It's your Soul. I affectionately use the term "HiC", my nickname for the Beingness that resides inside of me. He (I'm going to use "He" for myself as a male, although "It" is a more proper title) is my true Soul mate. He is the state of consciousness with which my human personality is learning to be One with The ALL.

"Christ Consciousness" or "Christ" is also a "title" like teacher, guru, doctor, Mister/Miz. It is a title given to people who have certain abilities or qualities--blessing qualities, healing qualities, a quality of peacefulness, compassion, insight, and the ability to communicate in a more conscious way. It comes from having reached a band or level of personal vibration that one can be assigned such a title. The label is not the thing. The Thing is the label.

Krishna, Jesus, Buddha, Mohammed, Lao Tzu, and others reached this level of awareness in their lifetimes on Planet Earth.

They are not gods, however advanced they may have been. They were/are simply more evolved beings.

CHAPTER 3.

Lessening Stress, Increasing a Sense of Well-Being

Let's first address one of the major benefits of meditation--lessening stress. Stress, that feeling of agitation familiar to all of us in response to the pressures of daily, modern life, is awful--pure and simple.

I look at my 30 something son these days and think, "It's no wonder he gets stressed out". He's got a high pressure, management level position which requires a 45-minute commute in each direction. He has two highly active and inquisitive sons. His wife is fabulous, works part time, and is at the center of his world. He plays in and co-manages a band that is beginning to make a name for itself in the Oakland/San Francisco music scene. He's in the middle of a remodeling project on his 1930s bungalow. The family has lots of friends who they enjoy spending time with immensely. He's an accomplished surfer. And then there's us, his parents, who live 20 miles away and are an important part of his life as well.

Sound familiar? Except for the details, some of which are related to his age and his personal interests, this list could be yours and that of most of the people you know. He manages all of these activities amazingly well but having so many balls in the air takes its toll. A toll many of us can relate to.

The impact of stress on our lives penetrates all aspects of our existence: physical, mental, and emotional. For example, according to Charles L. Raison, MD, clinical director of the Mind-Body Program at Emory University School of Medicine in Atlanta. "It's hard to think of an illness in which stress and mood don't figure," Raison is quoted as having said at WebMD. "We know stress is a contributor to all the major modern killers:

- Cancer
- Chronic lower respiratory diseases
- Heart disease
- Dementia
- Stroke (cerebrovascular diseases)
- New (or new strains of) infectious diseases (which attack weak immune systems)
- Intentional self-harm (suicide)"

According to author Hanna Braime, "Stress and anxiety wreak havoc with our immune system, leaving us susceptible to all kinds of nasties—particularly during the winter. Developing a regular meditation practice reduces the amount of stress-related chemicals in our body, and also leaves us less likely to turn to unhealthy coping strategies to deal with the stress."

Dr. Raison led a study that indicated that meditation improves both physical and emotional responses to stress. In the study, people who meditated regularly for six weeks showed less activation of their immune systems and less emotional distress when they were put in a stressful situation. Physiologically, it appears that one of the reasons for the improvement in these areas is that meditation "....reduces cortisol (the body's natural stress hormone) levels in the body" and, as a result, leads to lower levels of stress and higher levels of a sense of well-being.

We only have to examine the substantial increase in the use of anti-anxiety medication in recent years for proof of the impact of stress on the U.S. population and the use of potentially harmful drugs to cope with this "epidemic" caused by modern lifestyles. On the other hand, Stanford University researcher Emma Seppälä, notes that, "Meditation allows people to take charge of their own nervous system and emotions.... Studies have shown improved ability to [permanently] regulate emotions in the brain."

Here are a few more studies about the stress benefits of meditation:

- Decreases stress (https://journals.lww.com/psychosomaticmedicine/Abstract/2000/09000/A_Randomized,_Wait_List_Controlled_Clinical_Trial_.4.aspx) and Psychology Today's issue on Stress.
- Effects genes that control stress and immunity, Bloomberg, NCBI, American Psychosomatic Medicine

Journal, Journal of International Society of Psychoneuroendocrinology

- Strengthens the immune system which is weakened by stress, leaving us less susceptible to all kinds of illness, particularly during the winter. . (http://www.m.com/psychosomaticmedicine/Abstract/2003/07000/Alterations_in_Brain_and_Immune_Function_Produced.14.aspx) and (https://www.sciencedirect.com/science/article/abs/pii/S0306453008002199)

Conclusion

The beauty of meditation is that it can decrease the severity and the frequency of stress, and the resulting feeling of internal discord that accompanies stressful situations, large and small. Why is this? Here are some of my non-scientific thoughts:

- For some period of time, however brief a time of meditation we might undertake, the body/mind/personality disconnects from the three-dimensional reality that is our human lives.
- This pause allows us to return to our natural state of peace and well-being before returning to the stress inducing world each of us lives in.
- A mere 6 minutes, twice a day, as outlined in my new book, is a sufficiently long meditation to successfully disconnect and to cultivate the experience of peace and well-being. The HCM process is a fabulous way to begin your day in the right frame of mind before the anxiety of getting out of the door and off to work or before traffic madness takes over.

- In addition, the 6 second, brief mindfulness exercises can be used to reinforce the respite that comes with a morning meditation. For example, just taking a Sacred Breath, breathing in and allowing Spirit to flow into your consciousness, pausing, then letting Spirit radiate out to your world on the outbreath, can instantly put you into a moment of peace that can calm you for an hour.
- When Spirit, Eternal Life Force, Buddha Mind, Christ Consciousness, or whatever you want to call it, enters into the moment it cancels out stress and its causes for just that moment. It's like a short vacation that refreshes. Our vibration and our sense of well-being increases.
- While pausing for a moment or a few moments, our higher-level vibratory experiences are activated: a sense of calm, clarity, confidence, and lightness. The strangle hold of stress is loosened. After doing this for a few days or weeks, a more frequent sense of peace in the midst of chaos begins to seem possible. When it is experienced, the spell is broken.
- Higher Consciousness Meditation is a coping mechanism, pure and simple. It is a way to greatly help combat the incidence of stress and its effects.

I love it that science is studying and documenting the benefits of mediation. We all owe Jon Kabat-Zinn and his fellow scientists at the University of Massachusetts, a vote of thanks for the work they have done to show, through the scientific method, the proof of concept beyond the anecdotal evidence that has come down to us for centuries. Every few months, it seems, they push out the boundaries of the field into new discoveries and validations. While the steps seem slow and incremental, at times, they are laying the foundation for what I think is a transformation in the way we as humans experience our lives. A transformation that is evolutionary and will allow us to grow into our new selves as people and as a species.

This latter point was brought home in a report that was highlighted on an episode of the CBS Evening News. CBS News confirmed what we have all heard. Religious services continue to be attended less and less by the U.S. population. More and more people are saying "I'm Spiritual, not religious".

The most interesting thing that was said in this piece is that 5 years ago about 53% of adults in this country said that they experienced peace and well-being at least once per month and that today the figure is 60%. I was amazed. I would have thought the percentage to be closer to 20 than 60. Lots of folks are having at least a glimpse into what I like to call Five-Dimensional Reality, that Place that we all know, where peace and well-being reside. Where the experience of peace and well-being is a common occurrence.

This indicates to me that we are in fact evolving as a species, and perhaps faster than any of us are aware, into a new species increasingly comfortable with higher vibrational experiences: love, peace, joy, happiness, and the like.

CHAPTER 4

Physical, Mental, Emotional, Spiritual Health and Other Benefits

Meditation has many benefits. Amazing benefits, I would say, after compiling this list. According to Wikipedia there are over 3,000 scientific studies on the benefits of meditation. Check the list below or in Wikipedia to see if your condition or concern is among them.

These benefits are best experienced through a *regular meditation practice*. The length of your practice isn't as important as the frequency; you're far more likely to experience the many benefits if you meditate for five to 10 minutes a day, 5 days a week than if you squeeze your meditation into a 30-minute session once a week.

Also, the more you meditate, the more you seem to benefit, research studies (ScienceDirect.com) suggests.

Physical Health and Well-Being

Many of the scientific studies that have been done in recent years have been on the subject of improved health, improvement in the condition of a wide range of maladies, and preventative measures that improve overall wellness.

The following list of maladies have been found to positively respond to meditation (links included):

- Meditation reduces risk of **heart disease and stroke,** Time Magazine, American Heart Association, HealthCentral . And reduces thickening of coronary arteries (Stroke, March 2000) as well as reduce atherosclerosis (American Journal of Cardiology, April 2002). **Half of all-American adults have heart disease, most with high blood pressure.**
- Can reduce **myocardial ischemia** (American Journal of Cardiology, May 1996)
- Reduces the **heart rate, blood pressure and respiratory** rate by inducing relaxation. Improved breathing helps oxygenate the body more effectively.
- Helps prevent **asthma, rheumatoid arthritis, and inflammatory bowel disease**, Medical News Today
- Decreases **pain** (National Public Library of Medicine) by reducing muscular tension and associated aches and pains. In another study it was found that meditation could reduce pain intensity by 40 percent and pain unpleasantness by 57 percent. Morphine and other pain-relieving drugs typically show a pain reduction of 25 percent. Its pain-relieving properties beat morphine.
- Decreases **inflammation** at the cellular level (Science Direct). (Science Direct) and (Science Direct). Uncontrolled inflammation plays a role in almost every major disease, including cancer, heart disease, diabetes, Alzheimer's disease and even depression.

- Decreases **inflammatory disorders**. In particular, it reduced levels of pro-inflammatory **genes**, which in turn correlated with faster physical recovery from a stressful situation. University of Wisconsin Madison, HealthCentral and Medical News Today
- Reduces risk of **Alzheimer's** and premature death HealthCentral
- Improves **sleep** (Harvard citation)
- Improves **fertility** by reducing stress (WebMD)--women were more likely to get pregnant.
- Slows the progression of **HIV**-- no decline in lymphocyte content the disease fighting white blood cells
- Helps reduce **alcohol and substance abuse**, Journal Of Alternative and Complementary Medicine
- Can help treat **premenstrual** syndrome and **menopausal** symptoms, The Journal of Alternative and Complementary Medicine
- Improvement in **fibromyalgia** and **psoriasis** symptoms
- Helps manage **cholesterol** (DoctorsOnTM)
- Help treat **epilepsy** (DoctorsOnTM)
- Helps you **stop smoking** (DoctorsOnTM)

Mental Health

Likewise, meditation has shown to have significant brain related benefits. It changes your brain for the better and improves brain function. Here are some of those benefits:

- Increases grey matter--more brain cells, (Science Direct) for better overall **brain function** as well as strengthening communication between different areas of the brain.

- Increases cortical thickness in areas related to paying attention (National Public Library of Medicine) What this means is that **brains age at a slower rate**. Cortical thickness is also associated with decision making, attention and memory.
- Improves **memory (Psychology Today)** and Science Direct)
- Improves **focus, attention, concentration and multitasking** ability (Springer.com), (American Academy of Medicine). (plosbiology.org) and (Science Direct)
- Helps manage **ADHD** (Attention Deficit Hyperactivity Disorder), reducing hyperactivity and impulsivity, Clinical Neurophysiology Journal
- "**Cognition** seems to be preserved in meditators," says Sara Lazar, a researcher at Harvard University.
- **Lengthens telomeres, the caps on chromosomes indicative of longer biological age** (rather than chronological) according to Harvard researcher Elizabeth Hoge.
- Generates significantly higher **telomerase activity** in meditators. Telomerase is the enzyme that helps build telomeres, and greater telomerase activity can possibly translate into stronger and longer telomeres.
- Gives you mental **strength, resilience** and **emotional intelligence**
  Dr. Ron Alexander
- It Makes You **WISE(R),** "Wise" issue of Psychology Today. According to one issue contributor, "It gives you perspective; by observing your mind, you realize you don't have to be slave to it. You realize it throws tantrums, gets grumpy, jealous, happy and sad but that it

doesn't have to run you. Meditation is quite simply mental hygiene--clear out the junk, tuning your talents, and get in touch with yourself. You feel clearer and see things with greater perspective." "The quality of our life depends on the quality of our mind," writes Sri Ravi Shankar. We can't control what happens on the outside, but we do have a say over the quality of our mind. No matter what's going on, if your mind is ok, everything is ok. Right now.

Emotional Health

Emotional, in addition to physical and mental health, is improved in meditators. Who wouldn't want to be happier and more positive?

- Psychology Today dedicated a whole issue to the benefits of meditation's contribution to boosting **happiness** **(HAPPINESS)**
- Similarly meditation increases **positive emotion** (Psychosomatic Medicine) and (Psychnet.org)
- Increases **optimism**--the meditating brain increases electrical activity in regions of the left frontal lobe, an area that tends to be more active in optimistic people
- Increases brain volume in areas related to **emotion regulation, and self-control** (Science Direct) and (PsychosomaticMedicine.org)
- Increases feelings of **compassion** and decreases **worry,** Stanford School of Medicine (also Stanford), Sage Journals.
- Decreases feelings of **loneliness,** ScienceDirect
- Decreases **depression** (Springer.com)

- Decreases and prevents **anxiety** (Liebert Publishing), here (Psychiatry Online), (Science Direct), (Doctors on TM & Doctors on TM)
- Increases **awareness** of the unconscious mind, which is important because the unconscious mind is the source of many of the feelings and behaviors we individually and collectively have, New Scientist
- Improves our ability to **introspect** (American Phycological Association) and for why this is crucial see this issue of Psychology Today
- Reduces **emotional eating,** DoctorsOnTM

Spiritual Health

The practice of meditation, whether traditional or mindfulness, is first and foremost a spiritual discipline. It promotes spiritual health by its very nature. The power of spending a few minutes a day connecting with your body and your mind is powerful. Connecting with your Soul, the core purpose of Higher Consciousness Meditation, is transformational for those who have not had that experience, and growth inducing for those who have.

Meditation's spiritual benefits include (my non-scientific opinions):

- Promotes inner **peace, love, joy, aliveness, compassion, gratitude,** and more. It helps us address some fundamental questions like "Who am I?", "Why am I here?", and "How do I grow and evolve?"
- Helps us be **more awake and aware**
- Fosters a feeling of "**wholeness**". Doing so produces this innate sense of well-being that could been described as oneness, stability, grounded-ness, a sense of

perspective, and self-connection. In a world where most of our time is spent focusing on external activities, taking even a few minutes to reconnect with our internal feelings and sensations can change our experience of the outer world.
- Enables us to deal more effectively with life's ups and downs, twists, and turns.

Social Life and Interpersonal Relationships

Psychology Today dedicated a whole issue to **SOCIAL LIFE**. Meditation fundamentally increases our sense of connection to others. Among the benefits cited:

- Increases **social connection** and **emotional intelligence** (Psychnet.org) and (Psychnet.org)
- Makes us more **compassionate** (Stanford University) and (Psychological Science) and (David Esteno)
- Improves **empathy** and **positive relationships**, ScienceDaily, NCBI, PLOSOne.org
- Makes us feel **less lonely** (Science Direct)
- Reduces **social isolation,** American Psychological Association

Work and Personal Productivity

It's easy to say that many of the benefits already mentioned are also work related. Here are some key ones, including some that have already been mentioned, and an extended discussion of creativity, one of the most needed and sought-after business skills.

- Increases **focus and attention.** (Plsobiology.org) and (Science Direct), (American College of Medicine), (Springer.com)
- Improves **Productivity** (by doing "nothing")
- Improves ability to **multitask** (American College of Meditation) (mentioned above)
- There is some controversy about **multitasking**. Multitasking is not only a dangerous productivity myth, but it's also a source of stress. Meditation can also prevent you from falling in the trap of multitasking too often.
- Improves **information processing** and **decision-making,** UCLA Newsroom
- Improves the ability to be **creative** & think outside the box (U.C. Santa Barbara)**,** fostering divergent thinking. The Journal of Alternative and Complementary Medicine
- From the Harvard Review "Google's most popular mindfulness course, "Search Inside Yourself," offered since 2007, has thousands of alumni. Google believes that these mindfulness programs teach **emotional intelligence**, which helps people **better understand their**

  colleagues' motivations. They also boost resilience to stress and improve mental focus. Participants of the "Search Inside Yourself" program report being **calmer, more patient, and better able to listen**. They also say the program helped them better handle stress and defuse emotions."

CHAPTER 5.

Creativity and Problem Solving

My writing and my business consulting both require substantial creativity. While there are times that I find myself up against a creative block, taking a moment to break away and do a short meditation or use a mindfulness technique will usually help me move past the block. However, I find meditation to be most useful in my ability to be more creative.

When I sit down to write, for example, I will usually take a few moments to do my Higher Consciousness Meditation process and get into an elevated state of Awareness. From this Place words often just seem to flow through my fingers and onto the computer screen. Sometimes I can't keep up with the thoughts that are flowing so rapidly. And I don't worry about spelling—I edit later. There are times when 30 minutes will go by without a pause. There are times when the best thing to do to keep up with the flow is to make bullet points when the thoughts occur and go back later to fully develop the article or chapter. The key is having an intent to write and getting into that state from which creativity flows.

My intent frequently generates flashes of inspiration that occur throughout the day. I keep 3 x 5 cards scattered around the house so that I can pick one up immediately and write my thoughts down. Ideas that occur might be something that I have been thinking about and they frequently come as fully developed thought/feeling concepts that a few words or a sentence can capture.

The same with my business consulting. Creative leaps and problem solving are among the most valuable skills I have to offer my clients. My process often begins with gathering information from the client and a bit of research to define the problem or challenge. With the client or by myself, the next step involves exploring options and possibilities. Here is where creativity and problem solving are often involved. If with my client, we'll brainstorm for a bit to get warmed up. I will usually then ask for a pause, go to the bathroom, get a glass of water, or otherwise give myself an excuse to get quiet and go into a State of Higher Consciousness. (With a few of my clients, we do this together.) And then back to brainstorming. Almost always the creative idea or solution to the problem emerges.

Meditation or mindfulness exercises are a great way to become more creative in business (or in one's personal life, for that matter). The key is getting into that State of Awareness from which inspiration can flow, where a spark can cross the peaceful gap between thoughts.

CHAPTER 6.

Attract Good People, Things, and Circumstances

It my opinion, not shared by everyone in the meditation community, that meditation naturally helps us to attract good people, things, and circumstances. It has been my experience that the things I need are often attracted to me. You may be familiar with one or the other schools of prosperity which promise that you can have the things you want. One of the ones I have taken a look at has been spawned by the movie and book, The Secret-- a compilation of things that have been said for centuries about how to create prosperity, plus author Rhonda Byrne's creative spin on the subject.

A fundamental precept of The Secret is that you can have anything you want if you can "Decide what *you want*. Believe *you can have* it. Believe you deserve it. Believe it's possible for you," according to Ms. Byrne. This fundamental precept is generalized as the Law of Attraction. Some even claim that it is possible to manifest a new BMW in your driveway tomorrow if you can get into the proper state of mind or receptivity. Or by properly visualizing. The car might come by having an idea that makes you the money for the car. Or, it just appears. (A bit farfetched, wouldn't you say? Well, maybe not the idea that makes you the money to "manifest" that four wheeled chariot, but certainly the mysterious appearance. More about that later.)

It's my contention, though, that manifesting things and the Law of Attraction is down stream of, or ruled by, the Law of Vibration, which states that "like begets like" or "like is attracted to like". Not like a magnet, exactly, but because alike things like to hang out together. My wife and I like to hang out together, partially because we vibrate at a similar frequency. In addition, when I am a higher state of consciousness, people seem to smile around me more, the air feels lighter, and things just seem to "happen" that reflect my State.

I think this is true, also, about the material things we have. I have stood in my living room, looked around, and realized that each thing in my living room wants to be there with me. And from that state of Awareness in which I am experiencing Oneness with the Universe, all of these things, in strange way, are Me. Capital "Me", Spiritualized Me, appreciates them having come into my life to be with me.

Before you think "This guy is a bit looney", let me say that others far smarter than me have said the same things. Hermes Trismegistus, in Ancient Egypt, said "Every Cause has its Effect; every Effect has its Cause". In other words, nothing ever happens by chance. If something happens to you, you caused (attracted) it. Judaism has long held the belief that "What we think is what we get". Similarly, the Buddha said, "All that we are is the result of what we have thought". In the Christian texts—Jesus says, "Thy Father in Heaven, He knowest you have need of these things. And it is His good pleasure to give them to you". Lau Tzu, author of the I Ching, says "To the mind that is still, the whole universe surrenders."

I now know more about what they mean than I used to when I took their sayings literally. The Father Jesus was talking about, God, is not a being on a throne somewhere, that will reward us with our fondest wish if we just pray or beg in just the right way or be a "good" person. I think he was talking about the idea that God, or The ALL, knows you have need of these "things", both physical food and Spiritual Food, and that they come to us more easily when we are in an elevated State of Mind because of the Law of Vibration.

"Ask, and it will be given you" Jesus says. We will naturally have the oxygen we need to breathe. We don't even have to ask for that. Naturally, we will, to satisfy the rules of Planet Earth, figure out some way to feed and clothe ourselves. Wherever you end up in life, whatever circumstances you find yourself in, your human self will always want more of something that you feel you don't have. A better coat, a better airplane. These things are given you. I would say these "things" are attracted to us and we attract them. "Like is attracted to like."

More importantly, though, are the Spiritual Things we can have: peace, love, joy, well-beingness, compassion, a moment of inspiration, a fabulous meditation, amazing companions in life, an awareness of your own Higher Consciousness and even awareness of The ALL. "Ask, and these things will be given you. Seek and you shall find." Seek peace, find a way to get There, and it will be yours.

How? That is the Question.

How to get There? How to get into that State of Mind where both Spiritual and material things come to you? The Place where the Law of Vibration works for you? Where you become the Law of Vibration? Before addressing the "how", there is one more thing to discuss. The ego. Your ego. That ego/mind/body that is our human tool to survive. That wishes for more and seeks it out. That wants to make things happen. This tool is a two-edged sword of love/hate, good/bad, light/dark. A creative force for good and a creative force for evil.

Let's face it, this ego has an insatiable appetite for more, more, more. It is driven by a desire to survive and dominate or control our circumstances. And this desire body wants what it wants, whatever that is. Each of us has our own individual "desire body", full to overflowing with all the things which we want that we think will make us happy, or at least comfortable. And this desire body will stop at nothing unless reined in by our conscience or our values. This which WANTS can be a bit embarrassing to admit to. Certainly, without conscience or values, or in spite of them, there many things that we do to each other as human beings each day, and throughout our history as a species, that are horrible, mean, hurtful, ugly because we WANT something.

This ego/mind/body can and will take the information in this discussion and try to turn it into a tool to get more stuff and a tool against others. It will try to use Spiritual Laws to cause a new BMW to appear in the driveway or rule the world, as Hitler did. It is unfortunate for the ego that tries to do this. Because even if the human appears to succeed in getting that which is wanted, it is never enough. If the "thing" appears it is quickly put aside for the next thing and the next thing. More, more, more. Better, better, better. Our desire body has to be constantly "fed".

The Law of Vibration will not work as a tool of the ego. Why? Because if we are in a state of ego desire, we are in a lower state of vibration. That which does comes to us is not ever fully appreciated. It will lose its luster quickly, or it may backfire on us. In a lower state of vibration, we will inevitably attract "things" (matter, people, experiences) that will be consistent with this lower state. This will only bring heartache and karmic repercussions.

It's important to understand this and work, instead, on Spiritual Manifestations. The Law of Vibration works better, with better outcomes, if our desires are focused on higher vibrational outcomes. Enlisting our Higher Self to participate in our process will do just that. Our Higher Selves know what we need, are ever with us and available, and respond best when we bring to our aspirations a sense of Receptivity rather than begging God or trying to manipulate spiritual law for human satisfaction. "Presence rather than preference" as some Buddhists like to say.

How do We Find that Sweet Spot from Which All Good Things Come?

Here is a list, and some references:

- Learn to meditate. Meditation is one of the best ways to shift into a higher vibrational state of mind. Receptivity can come if we quieten down long enough to allow this State of Mind to bubble up. Learn mindfulness.

- Higher Consciousness and Receptivity go hand in hand. A Spiritualized Mind, which is one of the goals of my Higher Consciousness Meditation process, shifts us from preference to Presence.
- If you don't like what you have, or see, change your vibration. Lower-level vibratory rates, ego driven aspirations, and gross personal desires, accompanied by greed, intention to harm, hidden agendas, etc. attract, or are congruent with, lower-level people, places, and outcomes. Higher vibratory rates attract higher vibratory people, places, and outcomes. A change of vibration comes with a change of mind, from human mind to Spirit Mind.

What's the Formula?

The interesting thing about abundance is that nobody knows the absolute formula for it. If they did and they shared it, everybody would be abundant.

The attempts at a formula run from:

- Visualizing something strongly enough that appears in your life.
- Summoning what you want--asking the Universe.
- Asking God for things, or circumstances, or deliverance from….. And even bargaining. "If you do this, I'll do that" or the reverse, "If I do this, I'm expecting you'll do that".

- Conjuring. Using a combination of words and feelings and/or adding "eye of newt" (Shakespeare) to a potion to create some outcome. Magic.
- Trying to turn lead into gold. Alchemy.
- Believing in only one healing tradition: allopathic medicine, holistic medicine, psychic healing, fasting, or.....
- Trying to work the "law" of manifestation—attempting to pull the levers or create a state of mind which yields a certain result.
- Or, my favorite, getting as close to my most elevated state of Higher Consciousness and trusting that Spirit will provide. "Consider the lilies of the field, how they grow; they toil not, neither do they spin: yet I say unto you, that even Solomon in all his glory was not arrayed like one of these," to quote Jesus again. Presence rather than preference. Realize that The ALL, Omnipresence, of which you are made, has your best interest at heart. This is because your best interest is in the Universe's best interest. Higher Consciousness results in stronger growth and evolution--the very nature of the Universe.

I like what Lao Tzu says about this subject in the Hua Hu Ching, companion to the Tao Te Ching many of us are familiar with, "As the mind settles inward", Lao Tzu tells us, "It expands, culminating in unbounded awareness". This experience, he emphasizes in the same work, is the key to everything good.

CHAPTER 7.

Why Does Meditation Work the Way it Does for Healing?

The fundamental question I ask in this book, and attempt to answer, is "Why does meditation work the way it does for healing?" If we can get close to the kernel of truth, to discern the principal behind meditations' efficacy, we will then have a principal that we can apply to every situation be it health, wealth, better performance, or any other issue that comes along in our lives.

I think that meditation works because it interrupts the momentum that gets build up within our biomechanical body/mind/personality in the direction of some problem. The problem begins for some reason. Who knows--genetic, environmental, karma, a dysfunctional childhood and the pain associated thereto, whatever?

While the cause within 3-dimensional reality can be hard to pinpoint, problems or conditions do occur, possibly involving multiple swirling causes. And when a condition starts it begins to loop. The problem gets bigger, causes the causes to amplify, and the problem feeds on itself. A loop begins to occur, kind of like when I say to Alexa on my Amazon device about a song I am listening to, "Alexa, loop it", and the song plays over and over.

I'll bet everyone reading this message will recognize the loop effect. Somebody does something mean or thoughtless to us and we begin to wonder what's going on. We try to figure it out and also begin to think of that person as a "_______" (fill in the blank). We go over and over the mean thing, and the person's motivations, and we can't get it out of our minds. The loop effect has begun.

We begin to weave a web of upset, negativity, judgment, accusation, and desire to get retribution. The story begins to take on a life of its own. We tell those close to us about it. We speculate together. We may confront the perpetrator for his/her rude behavior. An argument might ensue. More mass is added to the situation and the momentum intensifies. The loop is hard to escape.

Meditation is therapeutic because it interrupts the momentum. Sitting in silence and withdrawing attention from the condition, interrupts the influence of the condition. If only for a moment. The condition goes into abeyance. If for only a moment.

In addition, if as in Higher Consciousness Meditation, we, in that moment of silence realize our 5-Dimensional Nature, realize that Spirit is the real-life force that animates our human body/mind/personality, we allow Spirit to rush into the vacuum left by withdrawal of attention from the human condition. Spirit, rushing, is a healing agent, going to all corners of our human condition to elevate it to Soul level. And we become our true Eternal Beingnesses. If only for a moment.

Human conditions exist only on in the third dimension. They have no existence in 5-Dimennsional Reality. My diagnosed glaucoma is not a condition in my Soul. My existence as Buddha Mind is unaffected by the condition of my human eyes. The condition is really not real, except in my human eye's biological condition.

So far, my approach to healing my glaucoma has been to go to the doctor every three months to get my eye pressure checked, to meditate before I go and to use mindfulness exercise while I am there to interrupt the momentum of the visit's compelling but illusory nature. So far that my eye pressure numbers have not increased and that I am having no symptoms.

As I write this, I am realizing that the theory behind the medical treatment, the eyedrops and the eye vitamins I am receiving, is to do the same thing. To interrupt the momentum of the dis-ease, the condition of the biomechanical system that I occupy, to arrest or reverse the condition that has been diagnosed. Similar to arresting or reverse the condition with meditation. Although this hasn't been the case with this condition I have, the unfortunate thing about medicinal treatment of some physical conditions is that the side effects are as bad or worse than the condition itself.

In my case, I think both my meditation and the medication are helpful. That my Spiritual intervention adds to the medical effects. Each can amplify the effect of the other. Therefore, I do a meditation the morning before going to the doctor and I take a brief mindfulness moment when I put in the eyedrops and swallow the vitamins, which I also do every evening.

I can understand why certain conditions like hypertension, for example, respond to meditation. If you are hyper tense, meditation, becoming more peaceful, would seem an obvious helpful antidote. But it has surprised me that cancer, arthritis, and even psoriasis responds positively.

I've concluded that one of the significant reasons that meditation works for healing is that it consists of withdrawing our attention, and thus our human energy from a condition, allowing Spiritual energy, which is always there (Omnipresence) to flow in and animate the moment. Realizing that human conditions are merely a part of the illusory, dreamlike nature of our body/mind/personality's functioning renders those conditions less powerful. If only for a moment. If those moments come more and more frequently, the conditions become less and less powerful.

Deepak Chopra, founder of the Chopra Center and teacher of ancient (Hindu) wisdom teachings says this more elegantly and succinctly, "There is only secret to healing and it is enlightenment" through meditation. "And realizing that you are the Universe manifesting through a human nervous system and becoming self-aware." (Secret of Healing YouTube video, which includes a recitation of an ancient Hindu guided meditation or sutra).

CHAPTER 8

Amplifying the Natural Benefits of Meditation

For those inclined to take advantage of the benefits of meditation for healing purposes, I would like to offer one further message. My experience has shown me that it is possible to amplify the natural benefits of mindfulness meditation.

Undesirable conditions, like the ones listed above and others, respond, or more accurately, recede, by interrupting the flow of the condition with a pause and a break in the momentum of the condition, as explained above. The next logical question is "Can this interruption be amplified and made stronger". I think so. In fact, I think that is what Master Teachers who were healers did. Amplify their healing energy, interrupting the flow of their followers' conditions, allowing Spirit to flow and causing healing to occur.

With that in mind I have developed the following guided healing meditation that has served me well. It goes like this:

- Take a moment and a few deep breaths to allow yourself to slip into your Buddha Mind, your Christ Consciousness state of Awareness.
- Invite the person who has a condition, or with whom you might be having difficulty, into your Holy of Holies. Recognize the Eternal Beingness of yourself and the other by saying, "I acknowledge the Eternal Beingness of myself and the Eternal Beingness of you". (This will seem strange at first but remember that such contact with another is easy on the inner planes of Spirit that lie within us.)
- State, "And I also acknowledge that the condition you have (or the problem we are having with each other), has no power over you (us), other than the power we give it".
- Say internally, "Let's breath some Sacred Breaths together". Begin breathing a series of deep breaths, saying on the Inbreath, "Illuminate", imagining your inner Higher Consciousness is expanding and becoming illumined. And then say, "Radiate" on the Outbreath, allowing the illumined energy to radiate out to the other person. Imagine that he/she is doing the same with you.
- When you feel a little bit of a release, when you take a deeper Outbreath, and sense that the cycle has been broken, that is an indication that Spirit has flowed out and will do the work that It Will.
- Do not, I repeat, do not, proscribe what that work should be, what condition should be altered or how, or what the outcome should be. Have no expectations. This will keep your ego/mind out of the exercise. Just know that the momentum of the condition has been interrupted, even for just a moment, and that Spirit will be about Its

business. Some shift, perhaps ever so slight, has occurred.

- Thank the other for coming to join you and offer a "Be Well" to complete the process. Take one more Healing Breath and return to the present moment.
- (Thanks to one of my teachers, Joel Goldsmith, 20th century healer and mystic, for steps 3 and 4 in this process, and the use of the term Holy of Holies).

You can also do this healing exercise with just yourself and a problem or condition you might have. Just adjust the language. All these steps comprise a pretty thorough healing process. There are times however, when you might just say to yourself, in any moment you're inspired to or feel in the need of it-- "Illuminate" on the Inbreath, and the "Radiate" on the Outbreath for a time or two, until you feel that internal "release". That sense of release will the indication that Spirit has flowed out to do Its work.

CHAPTER 9.

Conclusion and Next Steps

So why not give meditation a try. Give the healing processes a try. See if they work for you. If they give even the slightest amount of relief, stay with them, and get to know your Higher Self. Spirit and science are with you. If my meditation processes don't work immediately, don't worry. It may take a while for the fullness of this approach to life to blossom. Or this may just not be your cup of tea.

My best wishes for your growth and evolution in Higher Consciousness. If you found this book helpful and you want to engage in personal growth and expansion of your awareness, take advantage of the resources that **our website**, HiC Meditation, provides. Go to the site HiCMeditation.com for lots to see and do: a blog (past, present and future), articles, poems, a "Healthy Home" product page and references to resources mentioned in this book and others.

Studies have shown that if an adult wants to learn something s/he will do so more thoroughly and quickly if s/he uses a variety of learning techniques, each of which supports the other.

Here are some offered at HiCMeditation.com to support you in your journey:

- Go to the site to sign up for our e-mail list. We'll send you the weekly blog post/ newsletter and let you know when each new book is available.
- Our website includes over 100 products we have personally found to be helpful in promoting well-being and encouraging a Healthy Home
- We will be establishing a Healing Circle group on Facebook within the next 18 months where you can join others in using our Healing Process together.
- We will be releasing other products and services over the next year. Stay tuned.

If you got value from this book please, please, please go and review this book. Many people do not know that a review, even a short one, is like gold to an author. Exposure by Kindle Books, Google rankings and additional book sales are strongly driven by positive, insightful reviews. Thank you!

CHAPTER 10.

About the Author, My Story

The series of books that I am publishing is based on my study of spiritual matters over the past 46 years and the application of principals that I have learned throughout my life. In many ways, though, the impetus to write these books was born out of adversity and the need to dive deep into Spirit to deal with that adversity.

My trial by fire and my deep dive into Higher Consciousness began in earnest in early 2012 when I took a promotion and moved to San Diego to become Associate State Director of the San Diego Small Business Development Center (SBDC) Network. I had worked in the SBDC system, sponsored by the US Small Business Administration, for 19 years in North Carolina. I was exceptionally good at my profession and had worked my way up through the ranks with great success. San

Diego was my next stop to the top of my profession--State Director.

Unfortunately, my experience in San Diego was professional hell. The San Diego Network was being managed by a poor leader and manager. She had been running the program into the ground for nearly 10 years, abusing employees, manipulating money, and confusing her lackadaisical overseers with a smoke and mirrors game of monumentally devious proportions. Program performance was abysmal. I tried to find out what was going on with the program before I accepted the job, but nobody would tell me the truth. My wife and I were anxious to get back to California, after being away for 20 years. Both of our boys, their wives, and our grandsons lived on the West Coast.

For more than 6 months I tried to learn my new, complex job, and use my knowledge and experience to improve the situation. I knew what needed to be done, from my previous time in North Carolina, but my ideas were rejected. I ended up in a pitch battle with my supervisor over survival of the program. She began to blame me for all the problems with the program and she threatened to have me fired as a way of diverting attention from her own incompetence.

I blew the whistle on the sordid mess, revealing to community college officials who were supposed to be monitoring the program, what was going on. And thus, ensued another 6-month period in which an investigation was done, she got demoted and eventually fired from the program. Unfortunately, I was fired too as a "troublemaker" one week before my one-year probation was up. The program is now finally under competent leadership but is still at the corrupt, dysfunctional community college that is their host.

My next 12 months were exceedingly difficult. For nine of them, I tried to find a suitable job in my profession. I came awfully close to becoming a State Director and was in the final group of two candidates twice, but with no success. The same thing happened with Associate State Director and Center Director positions in California for which I interviewed. Each time I came up empty handed after traveling quite a bit and interviewing a lot. I'm sure it didn't help that potential employers would contact my former employer and hear… who knows what. I also filed a whistle blower action with the California State Personnel Board but lost after a hearing in which college officials accused me of incompetence and blatantly lied about numerous facts in the case.

Throughout this whole episode, my meditation practice was one of my key anchors to maintaining a sense of well-being. It enabled me to "keep my head about me while others were losing theirs" (Gunga Din by Rudyard Kipling). I was able to return over and over again to a reasonably peaceful state of mind, no matter what insanity was going on around me.

Finally, my heart softened toward those that I also saw as my tormenters. I began to recognize that they were acting out of personal pain and projecting onto me the things they were not able to accept about themselves. I could see that they were doing the very best they could muster under the circumstances of their work and their lives, which had nothing to do with me. It wasn't personal.

I managed to stay "in the moment" much of the time.

I went deeper and deeper into my meditation practice and began to have amazing insights and experiences, including experiences of illumination. And began developing a relationship with my

Soul, my Higher Consciousness. I began writing about my experiences, with no thought of publishing, but as part of my healing.

I came to understand the idea that has been taught by the world's Master Teachers for centuries about Spirit being Within us. That when we turn Within Spirit will come flooding to meet us began to make a lot of sense to me. In my case I think my Soul, my Higher Consciousness had waited lifetimes, many lifetimes, for me to begin to Awaken and has been a great, and patient, teacher.

This saga began to remind me of the "Hero's Journey" that Joseph Campbell speaks so eloquently of in his book Hero with A Thousand Faces. In the book he argues that many successful books follow the same storyline development. According to Campbell, the archetypical journey begins, inevitably, with the reluctant hero launching off into a new reality (San Diego for me); having difficult, life altering adventures; discovering treasure in a far-off land; and bringing the treasure or important information back to ordinary reality to share with the village s/he left.

In my case, I have done a very deep dive into my inner Self and have discovered the gold of my Higher Consciousness. I have returned to share what I have learned with the village, so we can all celebrate in our good fortune at what I have discovered. I now see the bigger picture of the whys and wherefores of my Journey and have found that I am exactly where I was led to be, where I subconsciously wanted to be, and that I created a scenario that allow me to let go of my previous life.

Now, right this moment, I am doing exactly what I should be doing, sitting here writing this saga. My tormenters were my liberators. They forced me to step into a world of the unknown that I only had an inkling existed. A life that is enlivening, and fun, creative, and ever expanding. I am beyond forgiveness at this point and over into "Thank you, thank you, thank you" to them for my new life.

Consider beginning to write about your own journey. I have found it very therapeutic, that it got me in touch with my Higher Consciousness and it turned into some books. Nice outcome.

Blessings.

SEE OTHER BOOKS BY THE AUTHOR IN THE NEXT FEW PAGES

And sign up for the newsletter at https://www.HiCMeditation.com for announcements about my next books, blog, contests, and more.

THE
MEDITATION
BOOK
The Essential Meditation Book for
Beginners to Reduce Stress, Find
Peace, and Improve Mental Health
PRIZE
WINNER
FESTIVALS
2020
BLAIR ABEE

The Meditation Book

Tired of meditation techniques that are frustrating?

- Meditation can be a difficult mind wrestling exercise.
- Want to use a meditation technique that is focused on Soul contact?
- One that is focused on Illumination rather than trying to tame the mind?
- Willing to try a simple yet powerful new meditation technique?

Would you like to:

- Be more **awake** and **aware**?
- Feel more **alive, joyful,** and **self-confident**?
- Experience more **peace** and **love**?
- Begin **healing** yourself physically, mentally, emotionally?
- **Attract** good **people**, **things,** and **circumstances**?

Book Available at Amazon Kindle in E-book and Paperback Form

PURCHASE NOW

THE
MINDFULNESS
BOOK
The Practical Meditation Book to Relieve
Stress, Find Peace, and Cultivate Gratitude
BLAIR ABEE

The Mindfulness Book

These short mindfulness practices are designed to put you into a place of peace and contact with your Soul. To, if only for a moment, remind you of who you are, an Eternal Being of Higher Consciousness, making it easier to cope with the world and to grow into your Self.

Among the benefits of mindfulness meditations are:

- They are one of the best ways to "get into the moment", become acutely aware of this present moment and the fullness of Now. Right here. Now.
- They can be done silently and quickly. In an instant you can find your Self having been "raised up" or "expanded into" an elevated state of Consciousness.
- A sense of peace descends, and all seems right with the world. Even if you are in 7:00 am stop and go traffic you may find yourself feeling tolerant of that numbskull who just cut you off without looking to see where you were.

John Kabat-Zinn's research at the University of Massachusetts Medical Center has shown that mindfulness exercise can have the following, significant, almost magical benefits:

- Create a greater sense of well-being
- Help relieve stress
- Treat heart disease
- Alleviate depression
- Treat anxiety, and many more conditions

The book is full of tips, triggers, and reminders to help you tap into Spirit.

The Book is Available at Amazon in E-book and Paperback

Cover and title are being changed to <u>The Abundance Book</u>

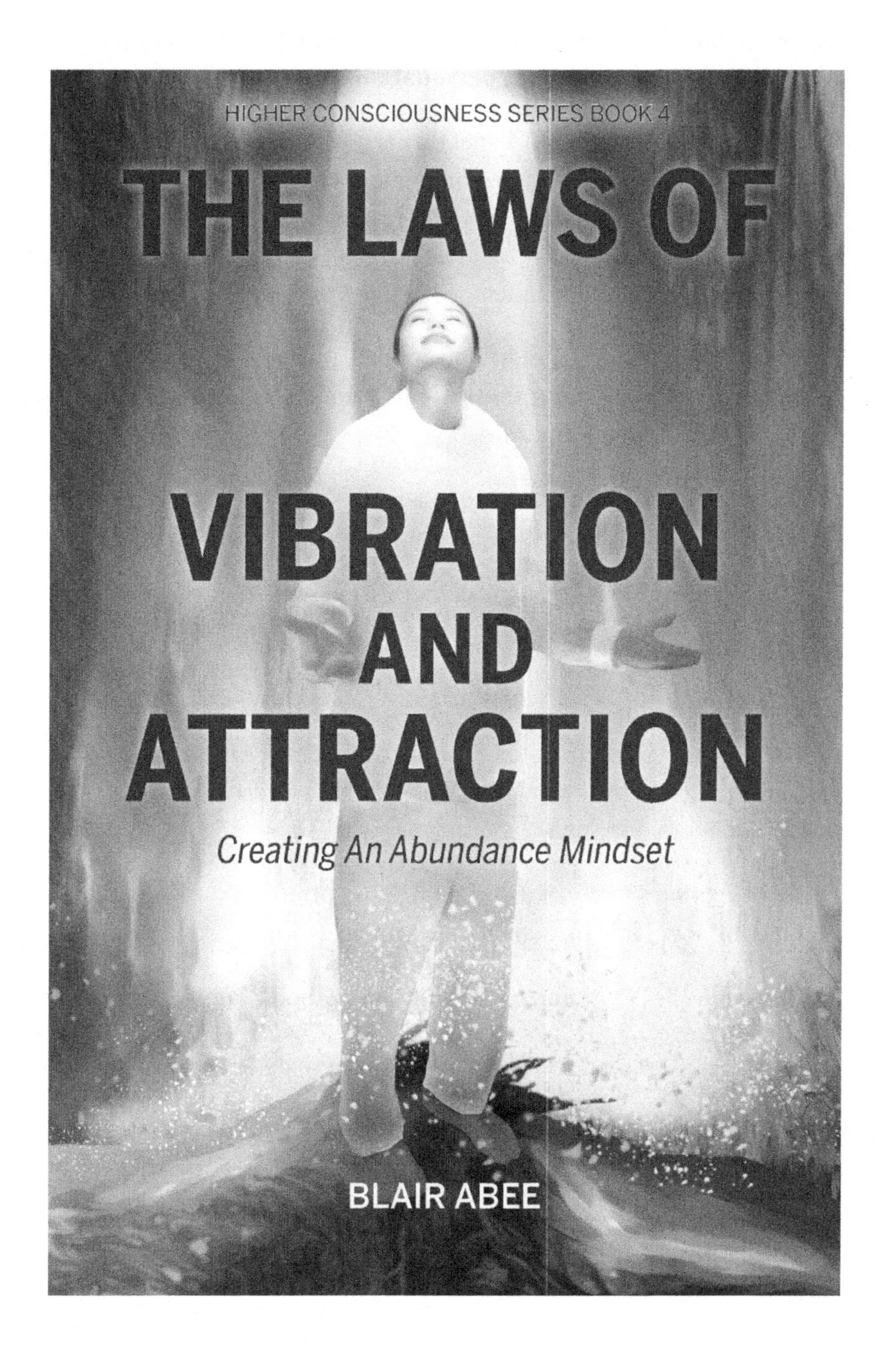

The Abundance Book, The Spiritual Path to Plenty

You were meant to live an abundant life, a life full of love, joy, peace, health, resources, and personal fulfillment.

Yet, we were all born onto a planet that is not easy to negotiate and which requires intelligence and cunning to create a sense of well-being for ourselves and for those we care about. Unfortunately, just getting through the day occupies much of our waking consciousness attention and personal fulfillment is illusive.

This book is an exploration of abundance and how the development of your spiritual side can help you experience your own, personal, true abundance.

The question of how to grow beyond a mere survival existence into a life of well-being has been the focus of many philosophers, authors, and spiritual teachers for centuries. Its most recent highly publicized exploration has been around the Law of Attraction and how to "have everything you want in life".

More fundamental than the Law of Attraction, however, is the **Law of Vibration**, which underpins the Law of Attraction. Also, more fundamental to having a new BMW appear in your driveway is the development of your Soul.

The book explores twelve key principals and offers very specific instructions about how to activate the principals for yourself.

Book Available at Amazon Kindle in E-book and Paperback Form.

Purchase Now

HIGHER CONSCIOUSNESS SERIES BOOK 6
HOMAGE TO SPIRIT
Poems to Elevate Consciousness
BLAIR ABEE

Homage to Spirit

Do you like spiritual poetry? Revel in Rumi? Then you will love this **San Francisco Book Festival award winner**. Every so often I get an urge to write poetry, and I just have to do it. Often it just comes pouring out. And I enjoy creating it as I read it. The **words just flow,** and they are almost always about a new realization I have about my spiritual unfolding. And unfolding and unfolding.

I never know what's going to unfold, until it already has. **Images come, inspiration leaps**, ideas flow out and onto the page, if I'm lucky enough to have paper around.

This book puts into verse many of the same ideas I have about humanity and the human condition:

- That **we are Eternal Beings** occupying extremely complicated biomechanical vehicles, but have so come to identify with the vehicle, and its needs, that we have lost sight of who we really are.
- That the **stress, unhappiness, and suffering** we all experience, mentally, physically, emotionally, and spiritually **comes directly from that identification**, especially the identification with the on-board computer, the human mind.
- That we can **reclaim our true selves** through meditation and other techniques designed to interrupt the flow of the mind's running commentary.

The fear thoughts and attempts to control the uncontrollable unfolding of the Universe instead of cooperating with Spirit for Universal Good. These poems capture my ideas is the **mystical language of verse**.

Book Available at Amazon Kindle in E-book and Paperback Form

PURCHASE NOW

Made in the USA
Monee, IL
10 September 2022